First, second...

Make playdough snails. Put them in order in a race and describe their positions to a friend.

Write the position of each snail in the race to the lettuce. Cross the ants that are in the wrong place.

There are four slugs in a race. How many different ways could they finish?

First, second...

	8th roll

1st roll

11th roll

15th roll

5th roll

9th roll

6th roll

20th roll

13th roll

16th roll

3rd roll

2nd roll

18th roll

12th roll

14th roll

19th roll

7th roll

17th roll

10th roll

4th roll

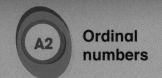

Make a line of coloured cubes. Describe the position of a cube for a friend to guess the colour.

Roll a dice 20 times. Write the number you roll each time in the correct box.

Dice.

Make a track game using 1st, 2nd...10th. Think of a different action for each space. Play it!

Comparing numbers

More than 45

Less than 31

Less than 22

1	2	3	4	5	6	7	8	9	10
11	12	13	14	15	16	17	18	19	20
21	22	23	24	25	26	27	28	29	30
31	32	33	34	35	36	37	38	39	40
41	42	43	44	45	46	47	48	49	50
51	52	53	54	55	56	57	58	59	60
61	62	63	64	65	66	67	68	69	70
71	72	73	74	75	76	77	78	79	80
81	82	83	84	85	86	87	88	89	90
91	92	93	94	95	96	97	98	99	100

More than 76

Less than 18

More than 105

More than 81

More than 116

More than 150

On a 100-square, colour numbers less than 25 and more than 75. How many did you colour?

Write three numbers to match each statement.

Is there a number on the grid with an equal number of numbers more than and less than it?

Comparing numbers

23 ☐

17 > ☐

☐ > 81

☐ > 32

24 > ☐

☐ < 77

☐ 43

52 > ☐

12 < ☐

61 > ☐

48 < ☐

Use towers of 10 cubes and loose cubes to make pairs of numbers. Which is larger?

Fill in the missing numbers.

For each pair of numbers on the page investigate how many in-between numbers there are.

Comparing numbers

64   89

90   79

84   100

125   110

151   115

95   105

139   149

140   120

99   105

110   101

Write your age. Write the age of an older brother, sister or friend. Write the numbers in-between.

Circle the larger number on each banner. Write two numbers that come between them.

Find pairs of numbers on a 100-square that have exactly nine numbers between them.

11

Adding to 10

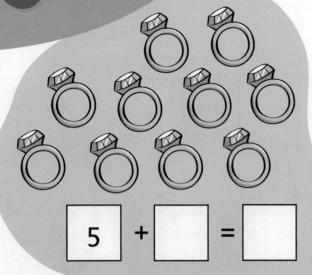

5 + ☐ = ☐

4 + ☐ = ☐

3 + ☐ = ☐

2 + ☐ = ☐

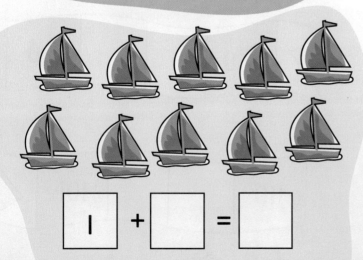

1 + ☐ = ☐

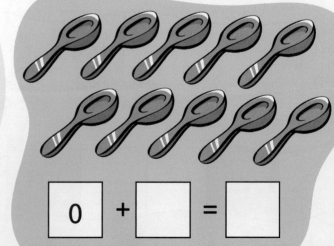

0 + ☐ = ☐

 Make 10 play dough rings. Split them into two sets.

Draw a line to split each set of 10 to match the additions. Write the missing numbers.

Find all the ways of writing ☐ + ☐ = 10. How many are there?

Adding to 10

 4 + ☐ = 10

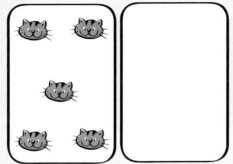 5 + ☐ = 10

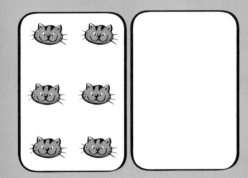 6 + ☐ = 10

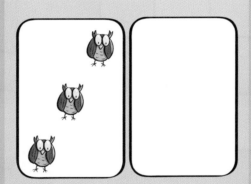 3 + ☐ = 10

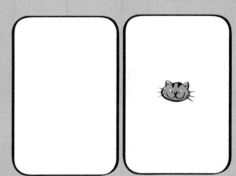 ☐ + 1 = 10

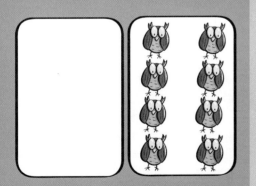 ☐ + 8 = 10

 ☐ + 9 = 10

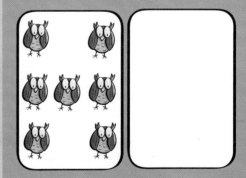 7 + ☐ = 10

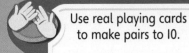 Use real playing cards to make pairs to 10.

Draw the matching playing card to make 10. Complete the addition.

How many ways can you make 10 using three cards?

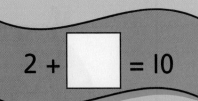
Addition facts

$2 +$ ☐ $= 10$

☐ $+ 7 = 9$

☐ $+ 6 = 7$

$5 +$ ☐ $= 10$

+	5	6	7	8	9
1					
2					
3					
4					
5					

$6 +$ ☐ $= 8$

$9 + 1 =$ ☐

☐ $+ 3 = 10$

☐ $+ 6 = 9$

$5 + 4 =$ ☐

$6 + 4 =$ ☐

$3 +$ ☐ $= 8$

Use 2 x 5 grids. How many different ways can you colour them using two colours?

Add the numbers across and down to fill in the table. Complete the matching additions.

Can you make 10 with two even numbers? Two odd numbers? An odd and an even number?

Adding three numbers

4 6 2 ☐

8 2 6 ☐

3 7 4 ☐

6 5 4 ☐

1 9 3 ☐

5 5 6 ☐

2 8 1 ☐

9 1 7 ☐

 Use 1p coins to match the numbers in each set. Find the set of 10 in each and exchange for 10p.

Add the scores on each set of three cards.

Three cards add to 15. Two of them add to 10. What could the three cards be?

15

Adding three numbers

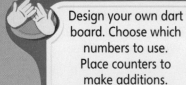 Design your own dart board. Choose which numbers to use. Place counters to make additions.

Find the total score on each dart board.

Find the best way to double each total score on these dart boards.

Adding to 20

4 + 6 + ☐ = ☐

2 + 8 + ☐ = ☐

7 + ☐ + 5 = ☐

9 + ☐ + 3 = ☐

4 + ☐ + 7 = ☐

☐ + 5 + 5 = ☐

6 + ☐ + 9 = ☐

7 + 3 + 5 + ☐ = ☐

9 + 1 + ☐ + 6 = ☐

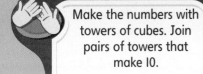 Make the numbers with towers of cubes. Join pairs of towers that make 10.

Roll a dice. Write the number on the dice box, then add the numbers. Look for pairs that total 10.

Dice.

Find ways of making 20 with three numbers.

17

Right angles

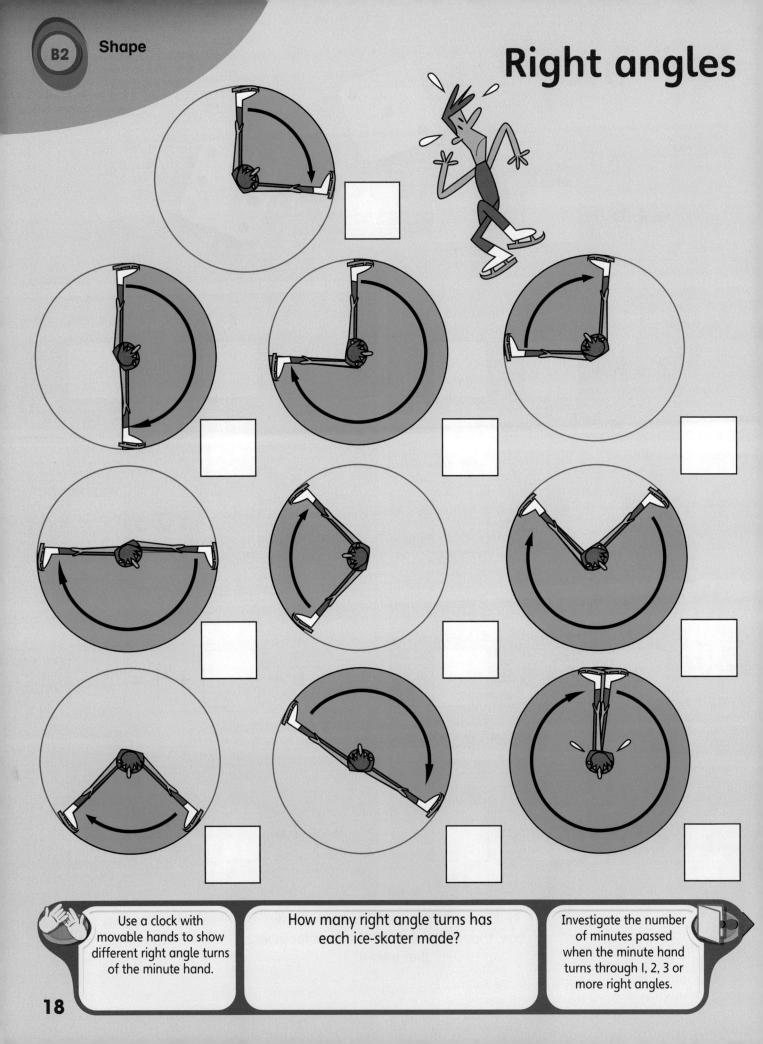

Use a clock with movable hands to show different right angle turns of the minute hand.

How many right angle turns has each ice-skater made?

Investigate the number of minutes passed when the minute hand turns through 1, 2, 3 or more right angles.

Right angles

Find some plastic shapes. Place stickers on the right angles.	Use a right angle tester. Colour yellow the right angles in each shape. Colour red the angles that are less than a right angle. Colour blue the angles that are more than a right angle.	Explore shapes that have I right angle; 2 right angles; 3 right angles...

Clockwise and anticlockwise

Take turns with a friend. Give instructions for one quarter clockwise or anticlockwise turns from a standing position.

Write 'c' for clockwise and 'a' for anticlockwise to describe each turning direction.

Look at the time. Imagine turning the minute hand through one quarter turn clockwise. What is the time now?

Clockwise and anticlockwise

In

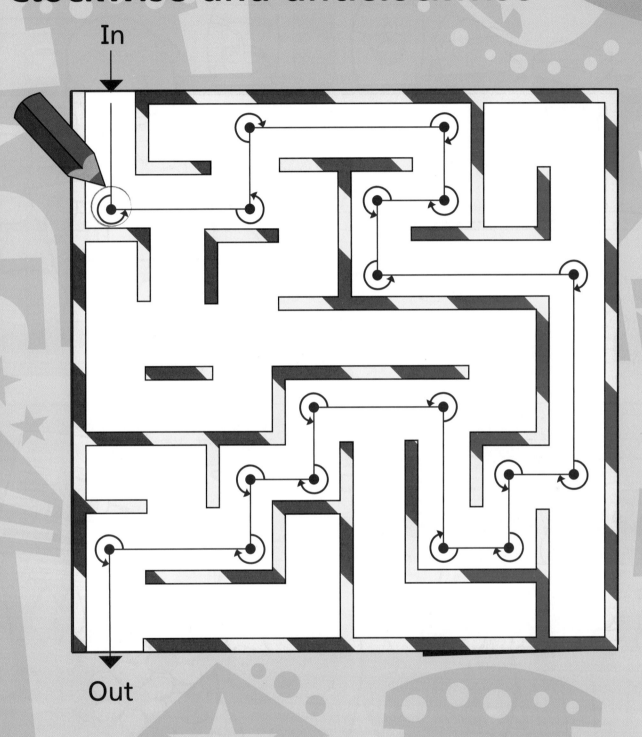

Out

 Draw your own route through the maze and label the turns.

Follow the route through the maze.
Circle in red the clockwise turns.
Circle in blue the anticlockwise turns.

Guide a partner through the maze using clockwise and anticlockwise turns. How many routes can you find?

Kilograms

100g 100g 100g 100g   100g 100g 100g   100g 100g 100g 100g

100g 100g 100g 100g   100g 100g 100g   100g 100g 100g 100g

100g 100g 100g   100g 100g

Nuts Nuts Nuts

Build or make something that weighs 1 kg.

Circle the objects that weigh more than 1 kg. Cross those that weigh less. Which objects do you think weigh exactly 1 kg?

Think of things that weigh exactly 1 kg.

Grams and kilograms

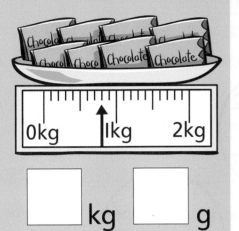

0kg   1kg   2kg

☐ kg   ☐ g

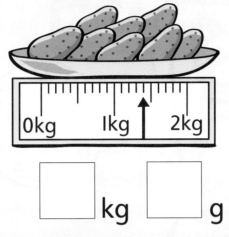

0kg   1kg   2kg

☐ kg   ☐ g

0kg   1kg   2kg

☐ kg   ☐ g

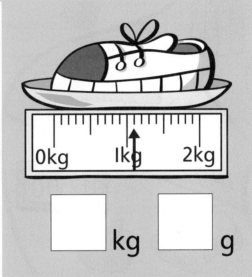

0kg   1kg   2kg

☐ kg   ☐ g

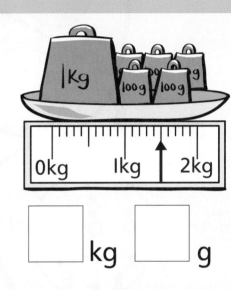

0kg   1kg   2kg

☐ kg   ☐ g

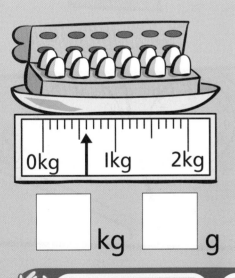

0kg   1kg   2kg

☐ kg   ☐ g

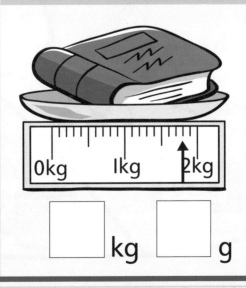

0kg   1kg   2kg

☐ kg   ☐ g

0kg   1kg   2kg

☐ kg   ☐ g

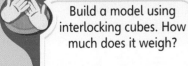

Build a model using interlocking cubes. How much does it weigh?

Read the scales and write the weight of each object in kilograms and grams.

Investigate the length of a tower of cubes that weighs 100g. Use this to find the length of 1kg of cubes.

23

O'clock and half-past

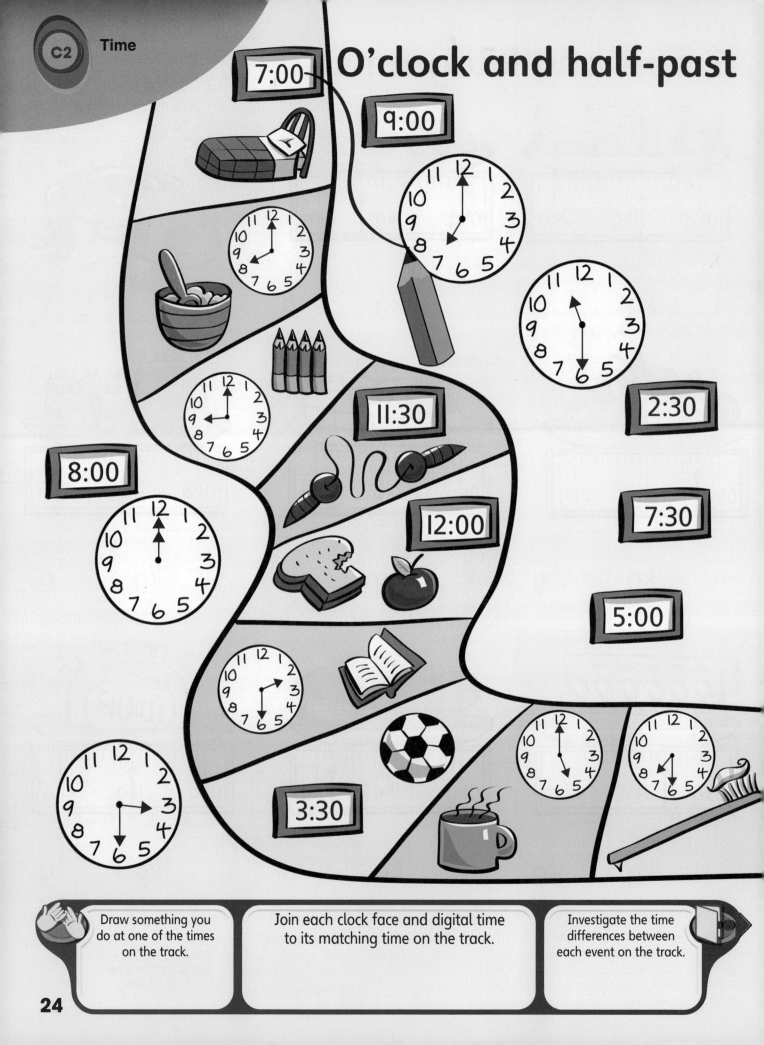

7:00

9:00

11:30

12:00

2:30

7:30

8:00

5:00

3:30

Draw something you do at one of the times on the track.

Join each clock face and digital time to its matching time on the track.

Investigate the time differences between each event on the track.

O'clock and half-past

:

:

:

7:00

10:00

1:30

9:30

Use a clock face with movable hands to show each time on the page, then say it.

Write the matching digital time or draw the missing hands.

Write the digital times half an hour later than those shown on the page.

Block graph

Colours of birds

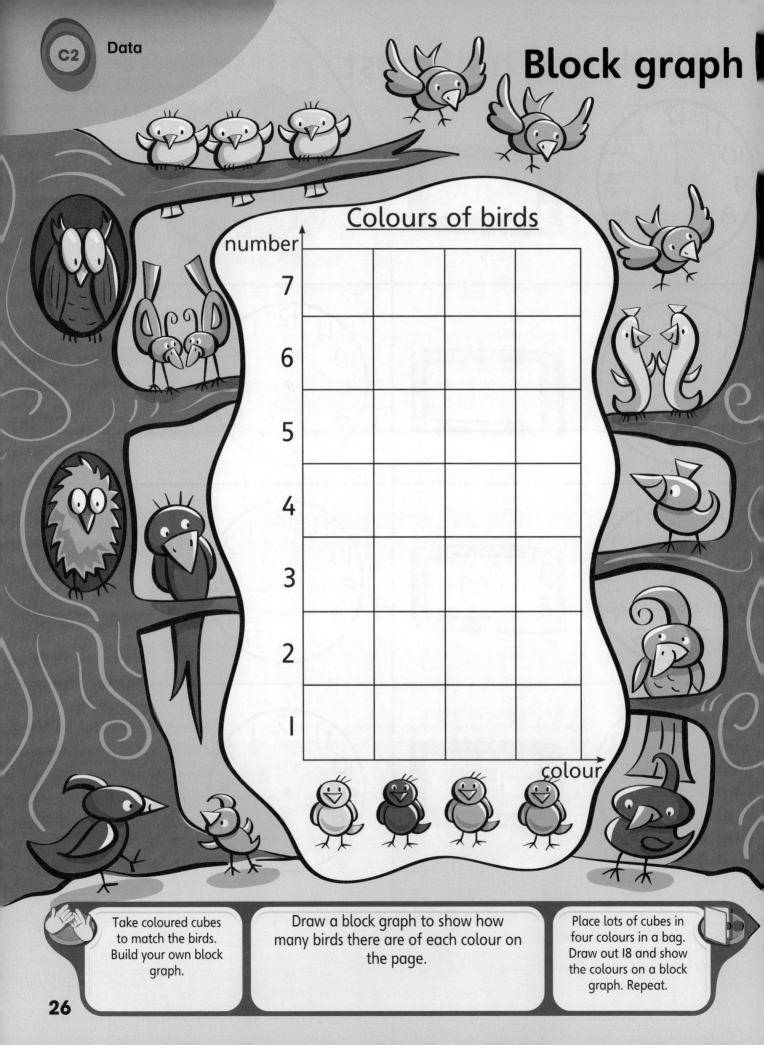

number

7
6
5
4
3
2
1

colour

| | Take coloured cubes to match the birds. Build your own block graph. | Draw a block graph to show how many birds there are of each colour on the page. | Place lots of cubes in four colours in a bag. Draw out 18 and show the colours on a block graph. Repeat. |

Block graph

number
of rolls

24 dice rolls

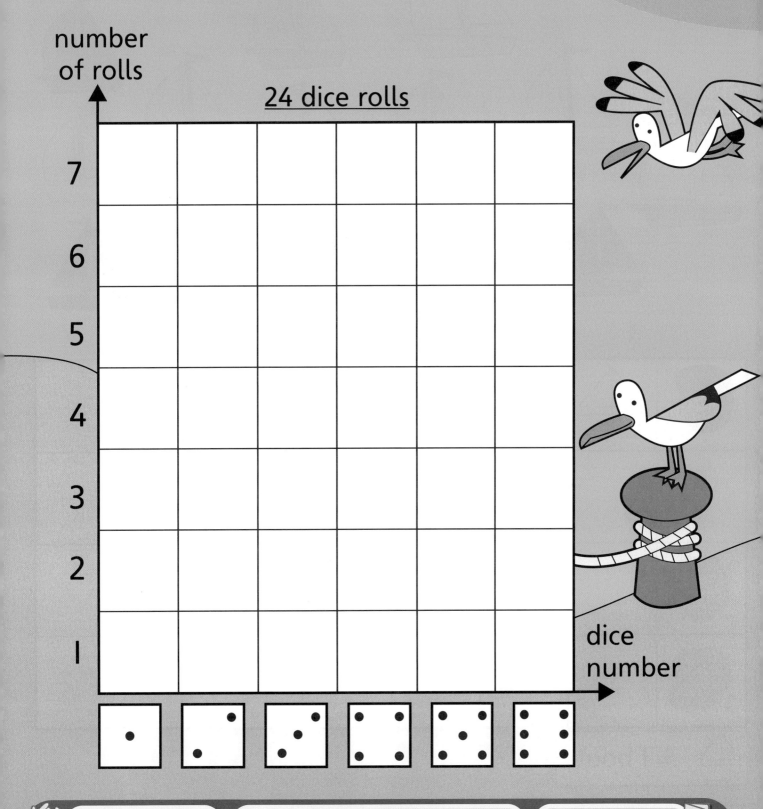

dice
number

Complete the activity using bricks as blocks and 1–6 number cards as labels for each column.

Roll a dice. After each roll, colour a matching block on the graph. Stop when three columns reach the top.

Investigate the difference between the total number of odd and even rolls on your graph.

Pictograph

Boat colours

⚫	△	△	△	△			

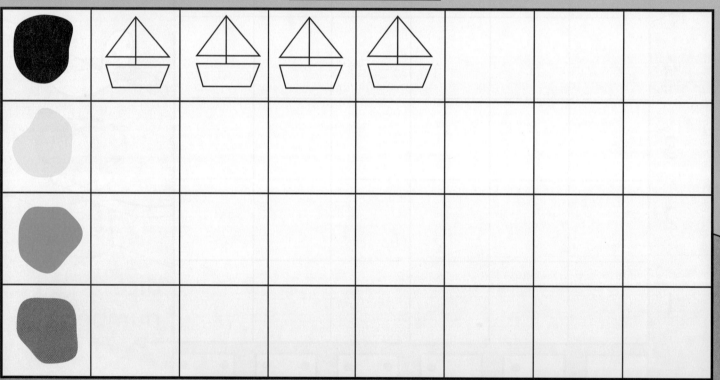

△ = 1 boat

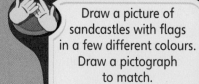

Draw a picture of sandcastles with flags in a few different colours. Draw a pictograph to match.

Complete the pictograph to show how many boats of each colour are in the harbour.

Use a large handful of coloured cubes to be the boats. Draw a pictograph using one picture to represent two boats.

28

Shape names

 cube

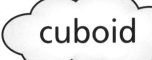 cuboid

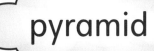 pyramid

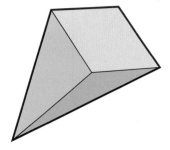

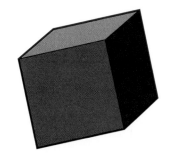

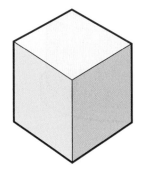

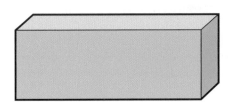

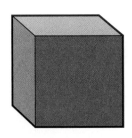

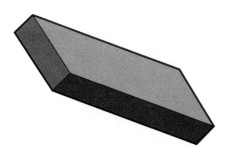

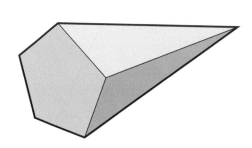

 Use Polydron or Clixi to make a cuboid.

Write the name of each shape. Choose from the three names at the top of the page.

Investigate the faces of different pyramids, for example a square and four identical triangles…

29

Cones and cylinders

cone

cylinder

_____   _____

_____   _____

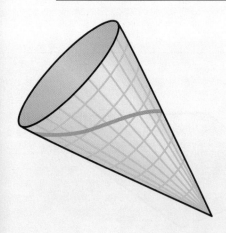      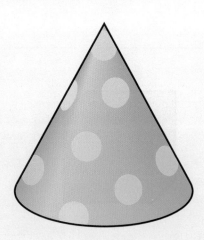

_____   _____   _____

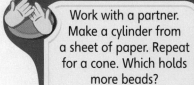 Work with a partner. Make a cylinder from a sheet of paper. Repeat for a cone. Which holds more beads?

Write 'cone' or 'cylinder' next to each shape.

List as many objects as possible that are cones or cylinders.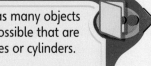

Faces and corners

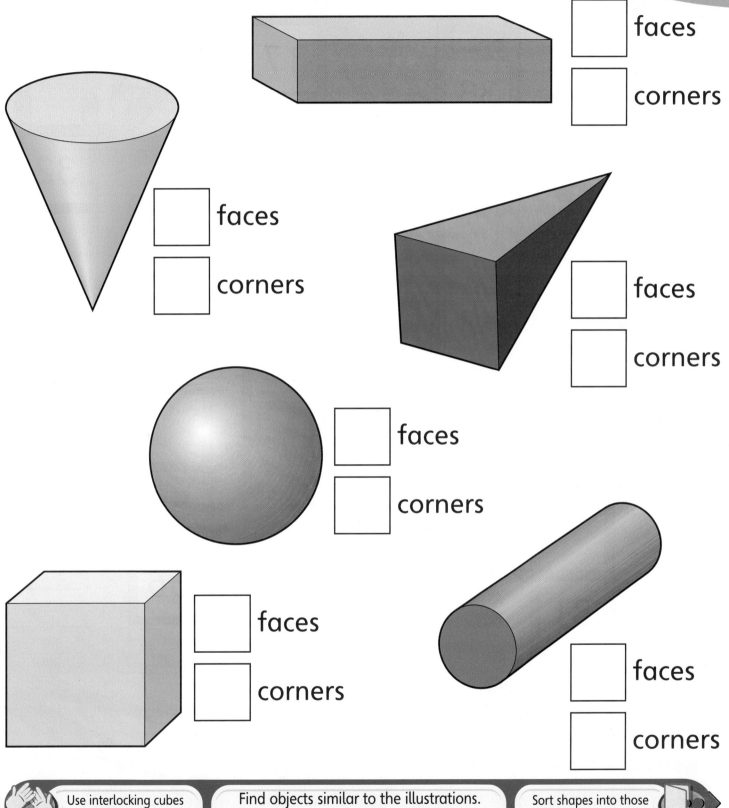

faces

corners

faces

corners

faces

corners

faces

corners

faces

corners

faces

corners

Use interlocking cubes to make different shapes with six faces and six corners.

Find objects similar to the illustrations. Count and write the number of faces and corners of each.

Sort shapes into those that have more corners than faces; more faces than corners; and the same number of each.

31

Counting back in 10s

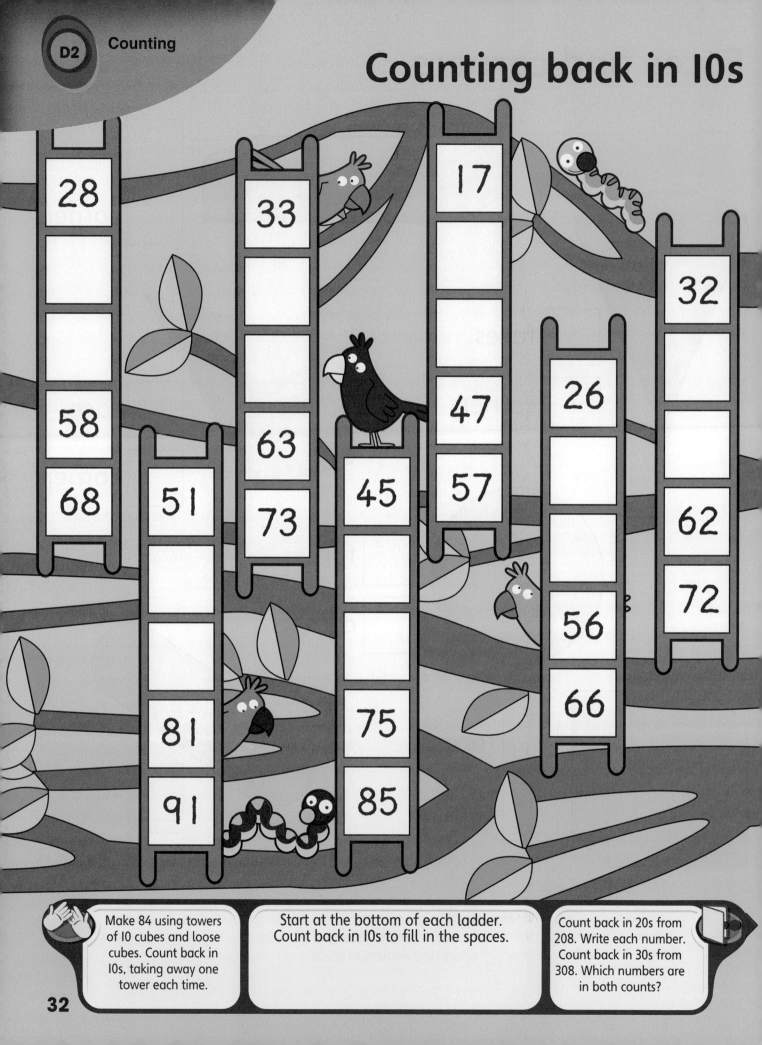

Ladder 1: 28, [ ], [ ], 58, 68

Ladder 2: 33, [ ], [ ], 63, 73

Ladder 3: 17, [ ], [ ], 47, 57

Ladder 4: 32, [ ], 62, 72

Ladder 5: 51, [ ], [ ], 81, 91

Ladder 6: 45, [ ], [ ], 75, 85

Ladder 7: 26, [ ], 56, 66

Make 84 using towers of 10 cubes and loose cubes. Count back in 10s, taking away one tower each time.

Start at the bottom of each ladder. Count back in 10s to fill in the spaces.

Count back in 20s from 208. Write each number. Count back in 30s from 308. Which numbers are in both counts?

Subtracting 10s

84 – 20 = ☐

47 – 20 = ☐

73 – 30 = ☐

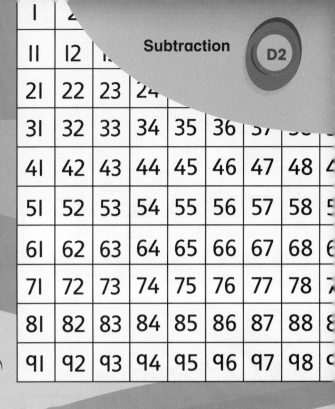

I	2								
II	I2			Subtraction					
2I	22	23	24						
3I	32	33	34	35	36	37			
4I	42	43	44	45	46	47	48	4	
5I	52	53	54	55	56	57	58	5	
6I	62	63	64	65	66	67	68	6	
7I	72	73	74	75	76	77	78	7	
8I	82	83	84	85	86	87	88	8	
9I	92	93	94	95	96	97	98	9	

69 – 30 = ☐

56 – 20 = ☐

92 – 30 = ☐

36 – 20 = ☐

44 – 30 = ☐

88 – 30 = ☐

63 – 10 = ☐

3I – 20 = ☐

28 – 20 = ☐

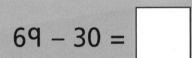

Use place value cards to perform each subtraction on the page. Which card changes each time?

Complete the subtractions by counting back in 10s.

Start with a number greater than 100. Subtract 20. How many times can you do this?

Subtracting 10s

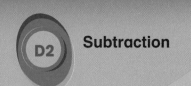

84p

30p off

78p

20p off

36p

20p off

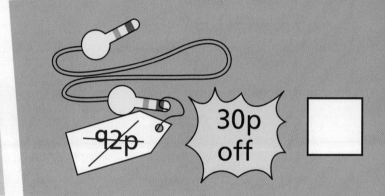

92p

30p off

83p

40p off

75p

20p off

53p

40p off

99p

20p off

Make each amount with 10p and 1p coins. Demonstrate the subtraction by taking away some 10p coins.

Write the new price of each toy by counting back in 10s.

Look at each price. Would it be better to pay the sale price or half price?

Adding 9 or 11

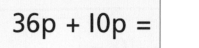

$$36p + 10p = \boxed{} \ p$$

$$36p + 9p = \boxed{} \ p$$

$$45p + 10p = \boxed{} \ p$$

$$45p + 9p = \boxed{} \ p$$

$$27p + 10p = \boxed{} \ p$$

$$27p + 11p = \boxed{} \ p$$

$$33p + 10p = \boxed{} \ p$$

$$33p + 11p = \boxed{} \ p$$

$$51p + 10p = \boxed{} \ p$$

$$51p + 9p = \boxed{} \ p$$

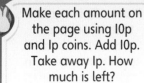

Make each amount on the page using 10p and 1p coins. Add 10p. Take away 1p. How much is left?

Complete each addition. Use the first addition in each pair to help you do the second.

Add 8p to each answer. Can you find a useful strategy to help you?

Subtracting 9 or 11

61 – 10 = ☐

38 – 10 = ☐

61 – 9 = ☐

38 – 9 = ☐

53 – 10 = ☐

87 – 10 = ☐

53 – 9 = ☐

87 – 9 = ☐

46 – 10 = ☐

75 – 10 = ☐

46 – 11 = ☐

75 – 11 = ☐

66 – 11 = ☐

32 – 11 = ☐

94 – 9 = ☐

47 – 9 = ☐

Use towers of 10 and loose cubes to make each amount. Take one tower away. Add one cube. How many now?

Complete the subtractions, using the first subtraction of each colour to help you. Complete the last four subtractions by yourself.

Pick a number greater than 50. Subtract 9. Continue to subtract 9, looking at patterns in your answers.

Add or subtract

1	2	3	4						
11	12	13	14	15					
21	22	23	24	25	26	27			
31	32	33	34	35	36	37	38	39	40
41	42	43	44	45	46	47	48	49	50
51	52	53	54	55	56	57	58	59	60
61	62	63	64	65	66	67	68	69	70
71	72	73	74	75	76	77	78	79	80
81	82	83	84	85	86	87	88	89	90
91	92	93	94	95	96	97	98	99	100

$28 + 19 = \boxed{}$

$56 - 19 = \boxed{}$

$61 + 29 = \boxed{}$

$39 - 29 = \boxed{}$

$45 - 19 = \boxed{}$

$93 - 19 = \boxed{}$

$36 - 19 = \boxed{}$

$84 - 29 = \boxed{}$

$17 + 29 = \boxed{}$

$23 + 29 = \boxed{}$

$51 - 29 = \boxed{}$

Use a 100-square and transparent counters. Where do you slide the counters to do each calculation?

Complete each addition and subtraction.

Start with 8. Add 19. Continue adding 19. What is the pattern?

10s, 2s and 5s

| 40 | 50 | | | |

| 8 | 10 | | | | |

| 20 | 30 | | | | | |

| 5 | 10 | | | | | | |

| 35 | 40 | | | | | | |

| 32 | 34 | | | | | |

Thread beads of different colours in pairs or 5s.

Count in 10s along the red trains.
Count in 2s along the yellow trains.
Count in 5s along the blue trains.

Draw more trains, starting at 0 and counting in steps of different numbers. Which numbers appear in more than one train?

Odd and even

1	2	3	4		6			9	
11	12			15		17			20
	22		24				28		

1	2	3
4	5	
7		
		12
	14	
16		
	20	
		24
25		
	29	30

1	2	3	4	5
6			9	
11				15
		18		
			24	

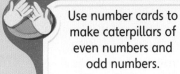

Use number cards to make caterpillars of even numbers and odd numbers.

Write the missing numbers. Colour all the odd numbers pink and all the even numbers green.

Draw different square grids. Number them, starting at 1. Investigate patterns of the even numbers in each grid.

Odd and even

3

12

24

19

15

20

42

23

16

Look at the page numbers in this book. Explore the pattern of odd and even numbers.

Each pair of houses has either both odd or both even numbers. Write the number that comes before or after to complete the house numbers.

Imagine houses in blocks of three next-door numbers. Investigate patterns in the numbers of the middle houses.

Twos

$2 \times 2 =$ ☐

$3 \times 2 =$ ☐

$4 \times 2 =$ ☐

$7 \times 2 =$ ☐

$5 \times 2 =$ ☐

$6 \times 2 =$ ☐

$8 \times 2 =$ ☐

Make smiley faces from playdough. Put sets of faces together and count the eyes.

Complete the multiplications to show the number of eyes hiding in each bush.

Investigate how many eyes there are in your classroom! Write a matching multiplication.

41

Fives

6 × 5 = ☐

☐ × 5 = ☐

4 × 5 = ☐

3 × 5 = ☐

☐ × 5 = ☐

☐ × 5 = ☐

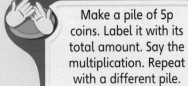

Make a pile of 5p coins. Label it with its total amount. Say the multiplication. Repeat with a different pile.

Complete each multiplication to show the total in each set of jam tarts.

Investigate which totals of 5p coins can be made with totals of other coins, for example 2p coins.

Multiplying

☐ × 4 = ☐

☐ × 4 = ☐

☐ × 4 = ☐

☐ × 3 = ☐

☐ × ☐ = ☐

☐ × ☐ = ☐

Match cubes to monster legs. Make sets of four and sets of three.

Complete a multiplication for the number of legs in each group of monsters.

A group of blue monsters has the same number of legs as a group of red monsters. How many monsters in each group?

Multiplying

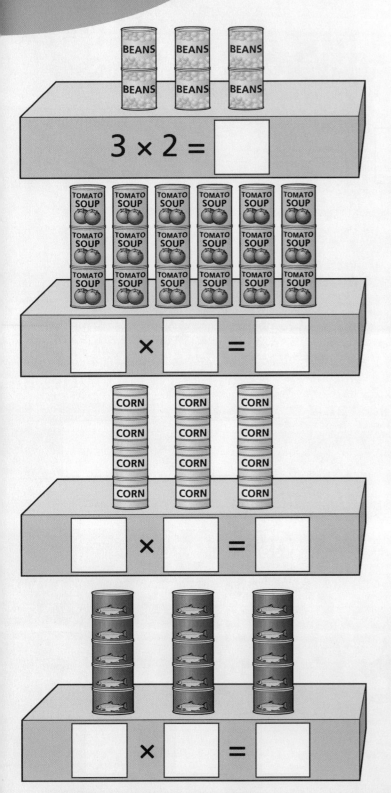

$3 \times 2 = \boxed{}$

$\boxed{} \times \boxed{} = \boxed{}$

$\boxed{} \times \boxed{} = \boxed{}$

$\boxed{} \times \boxed{} = \boxed{}$

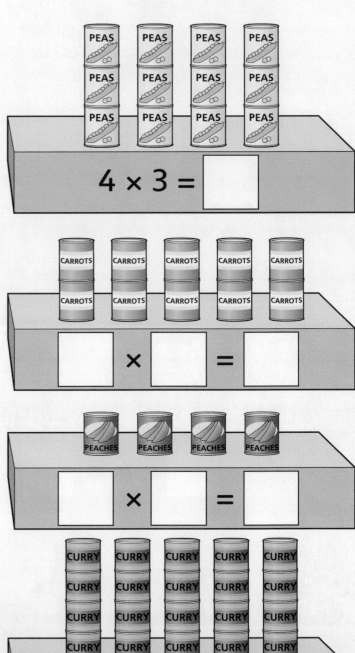

$4 \times 3 = \boxed{}$

$\boxed{} \times \boxed{} = \boxed{}$

$\boxed{} \times \boxed{} = \boxed{}$

$\boxed{} \times \boxed{} = \boxed{}$

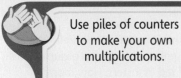 Use piles of counters to make your own multiplications.

Write a multiplication to show how many tins on each shelf.

Investigate different multiplications for a total of 24 tins.

Multiplying

☐ × ☐ = ☐
☐ × ☐ = ☐

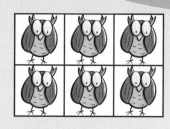

☐ × ☐ = ☐
☐ × ☐ = ☐

☐ × ☐ = ☐
☐ × ☐ = ☐

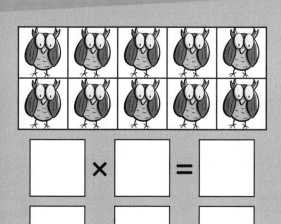

☐ × ☐ = ☐
☐ × ☐ = ☐

☐ × ☐ = ☐
☐ × ☐ = ☐

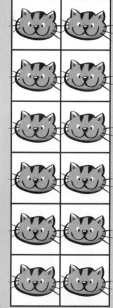

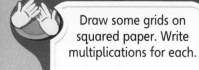 Draw some grids on squared paper. Write multiplications for each.

Write two multiplications for each set of stickers.

Which numbers between 10 and 20 can not be made with 2 or more rows of stickers?

Dividing

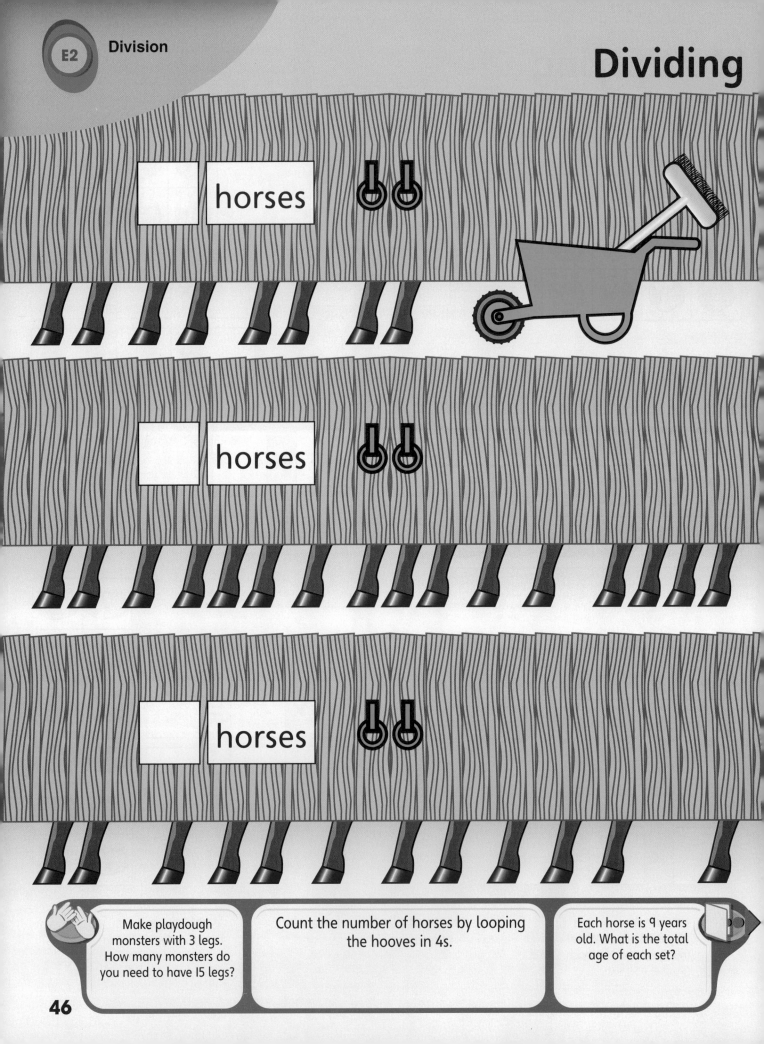

horses

horses

horses

Make playdough monsters with 3 legs. How many monsters do you need to have 15 legs?

Count the number of horses by looping the hooves in 4s.

Each horse is 9 years old. What is the total age of each set?

Dividing

$\boxed{12} \div 4 = \boxed{}$

$\boxed{} \div 3 = \boxed{}$

$\boxed{} \div 2 = \boxed{}$

$\boxed{} \div 5 = \boxed{}$

$\boxed{} \div 3 = \boxed{}$

$\boxed{} \div 4 = \boxed{}$

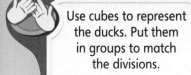 Use cubes to represent the ducks. Put them in groups to match the divisions.

Draw loops to group the ducks to match the division. Complete the division.

Investigate different ways of grouping each set of ducks.

Talk with your teacher about when to colour an animal.

The instructions at the foot of each page are written for teachers to explain to children. The core activity is written in the centre. The activities with the 🐾 icon provide a practical activity, often requiring the children to do or make something, while the activities marked with 📄 provide an activity for children who require more challenge.

Ginn is an imprint of Pearson Education Limited, a company incorporated in England and Wales, having its registered office at Edinburgh Gate, Harlow, Essex, CM20 2JE. Registered company number: 872828

ISBN: 978 0602 57639 4 © Ginn 2007
First published 2007
Tenth impression 2011
Printed in Malaysia (CTP-VP)

Abacus Evolve Framework Edition

To find out more about Ginn products, plus free supporting resources, visit

www.ginn.co.uk
01865 888020

Ginn
Part of Pearson

ISBN 978-0-602576-39-4

9 780602 576394